CW00429678

Electronic Keyboard
Grade 1

Pieces & Technical Work
for Trinity College London examinations

2011-2013

Published by
Trinity College London
Registered office:
89 Albert Embankment
London SE1 7TP UK

T +44 (0)20 7820 6100
F +44 (0)20 7820 6161
E music@trinitycollege.co.uk
www.trinitycollege.co.uk

Registered in the UK
Company no. 02683033
Charity no. 1014792

Rondo

from *Abdelazer*

Henry Purcell
arr. Joanna Clarke

Voices: Brass/Strings
Style: Waltz (not Viennese)

To Strings

Fine

D.C. al Fine

To Brass

PLEASE SET UP FOR THE NEXT PIECE

Greensleeves

Traditional
arr. Victoria Proudler

Voices: Pan Flute/Woodwind
Style: Waltz

PLEASE SET UP FOR THE NEXT PIECE

Own Interpretation

Caprice no. 24

from *24 Caprices*

Niccolò Paganini
arr. Nigel Fletcher

Voices: _____

Style: _____

PLEASE SET UP FOR THE NEXT PIECE

Dance of the Hours

from *La gioconda*

Amilcare Ponchielli
arr. Nancy Litten

Voices: Strings/Piano
Style: 8 Beat Pop

To Piano

PLEASE SET UP FOR THE NEXT PIECE

Romance de amor

Traditional
arr. Andrew Smith

Voices: Classical or Acoustic Guitar/Piccolo*
Style: ⁶⁄₈ Ballad

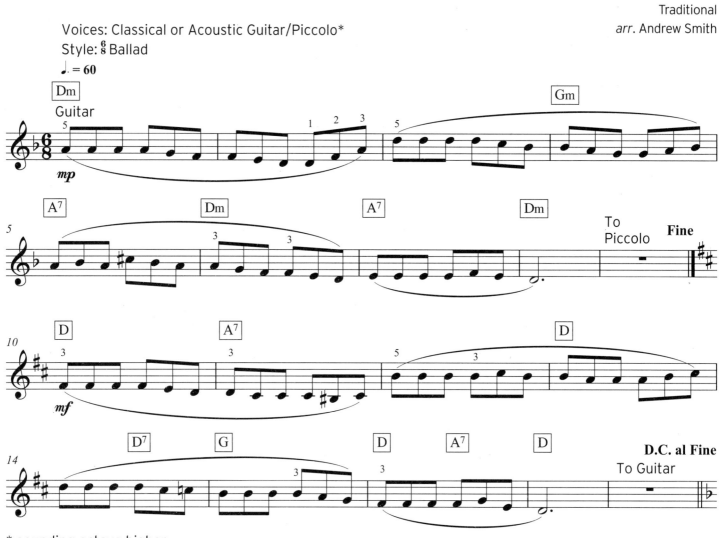

* sounding octave higher.

PLEASE SET UP FOR THE NEXT PIECE

This piece is published under licence from Andrew Smith.

La bamba

Traditional
arr. Nancy Litten

Voices: Clean Guitar/Brass
Style: Rock Cha-cha

*Number of bars depends on length of ending used.

PLEASE SET UP FOR THE NEXT PIECE

Karnak

Andrew Smith

Voices: Dulcimer/Clarinet
Style: March

PLEASE SET UP FOR THE NEXT PIECE

Improvisation

Southern Country

Nancy Litten

Voices: Guitar/Strings
Style: Country Waltz

*Number of bars depends on length of ending used.

PLEASE SET UP FOR THE NEXT PIECE

One Day Like This

Guy Garvey, Craig Potter, Mark Potter,
Peter Turner and Richard Jupp
arr. Victoria Proudler

Voices: Strings/Choir
Style: Ballad

PLEASE SET UP FOR THE NEXT PIECE

For the Love of Malkauns

Kuljit Bhamra

Voices: Piano/Oboe
Style: 8 Beat

PLEASE SET UP FOR THE NEXT PIECE

Technical Work

Sections i) or ii) to be prepared. Section i) must be performed from memory; the music may be used for Section ii).

i) Scales

The following scales to be performed in piano voice with auto-accompaniment off, hands separately (unless otherwise stated),
♩ = 70, *legato* and ***mf***:

    F and G major (one octave)
    D and E minor (one octave): candidate's choice of *either* harmonic *or* melodic *or* natural minor
    Chromatic scale in contrary motion, hands together, starting on D (one octave)
    Pentatonic scale starting on G and F (five notes)

F major scale (one octave)

Right hand

Left hand

G major scale (one octave)

Right hand

Left hand

D minor scale: harmonic (one octave)

Right hand

Left hand

D minor scale: melodic (one octave)

Right hand

Left hand

D minor scale: natural (one octave)

Right hand

Left hand

E minor scale: harmonic (one octave)

Right hand

Left hand

E minor scale: melodic (one octave)

Right hand

Left hand

E minor scale: natural (one octave)

Right hand

Left hand

Chromatic scale in contrary motion, hands together, starting on D (one octave)

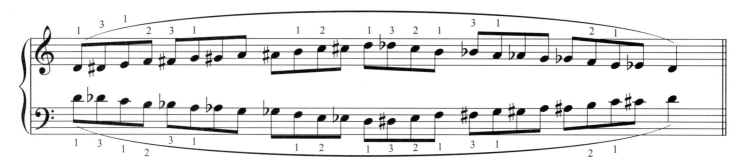

Pentatonic scale starting on G (five notes)

Right hand

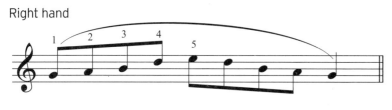

Left hand

Pentatonic scale starting on F (five notes)

Right hand

Left hand

Chord knowledge

The following to be performed with the left hand in piano voice with auto-accompaniment off:

Triad of F and G major, D and E minor (root position and first inversion)
Chord of F^7 and G^7 (root position and first inversion)

F major

G major

D minor

E minor

F^7

G^7

please turn over

ii) Exercises

Candidate to prepare all three exercises.

1. Chickens – bass clef reading and finger dexterity

Voice: Piano
Style: 16 Beat

Strutting [♩ = c. **80**]

Accomp. off (rhythm only)

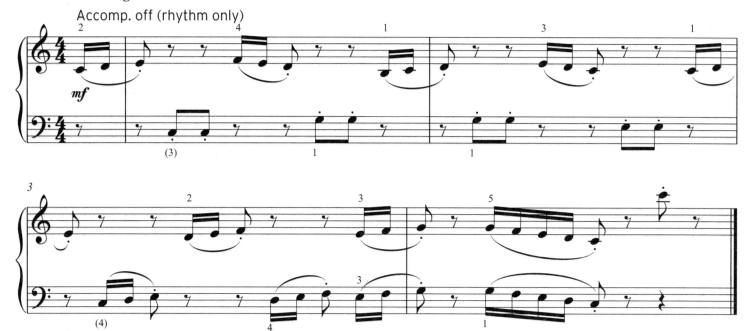

2. Bruce and the Spider – arpeggios and chord use [fingered chords must be used]

Voice: Harp
Style: Waltz

♩ = **150**

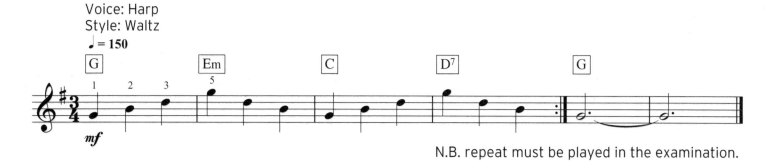

N.B. repeat must be played in the examination.

3. Yee-Ha! – using keyboard functions

Voices: Harmonica/Accordion
Style: Bluegrass

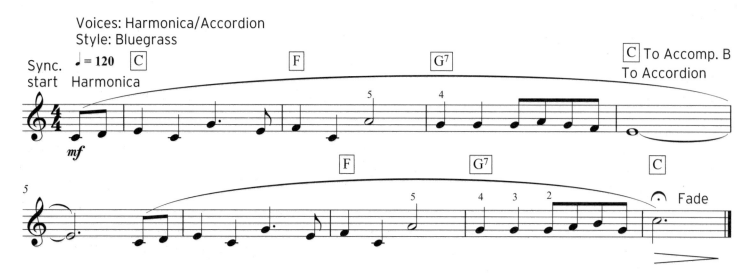